SPRING
Coloring & Activity Book

BENDON™

©2011
Bendon Publishing International, Inc.
Ashland, OH 44805
www.bendonpub.com

Connect the dots.

How Many Words?

Make as many words as you can out of the word or words below.

BUTTERFLIES

_____

_____

_____

_____

_____

_____

_____

_____

_____

SPRING WORD SCRAMBLE

Unscramble the spring words below.

BBARIT

_____

RABBIT

OTRRAC

_____

CARROT

PIH POH

_____

HIP HOP

Finish the picture.

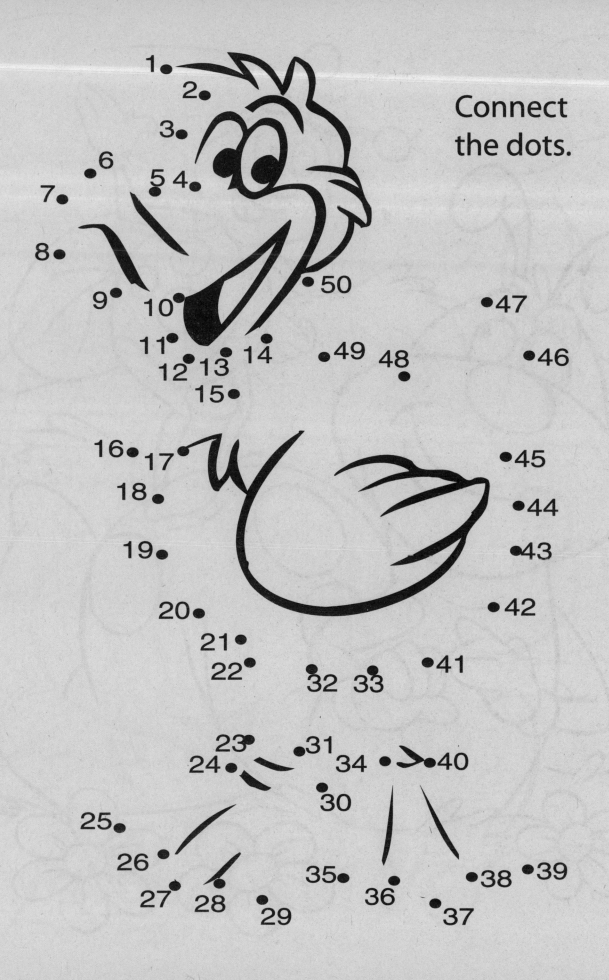

Connect
the dots.

Draw the Faces!

Which flower is different?

1.

2.

3.

4.

5.

6.

ANSWER: 4

Connect the dots.

Use the grid to draw the picture.

Which one does not belong with the others?

Help the rabbit find a path through the garden

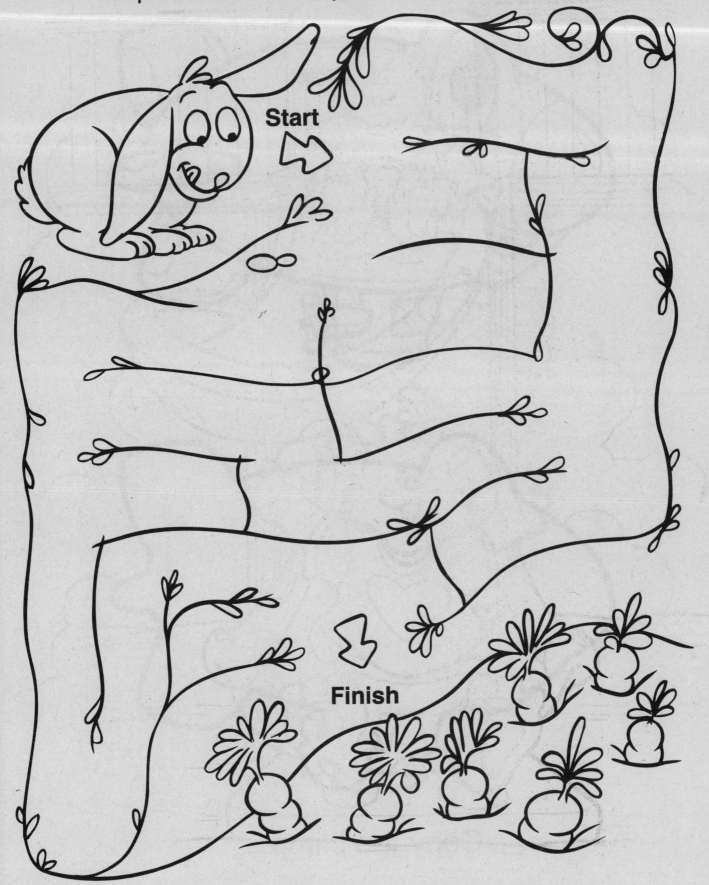

Start

Finish

Copy the blimp.

Use the grid to draw the character.

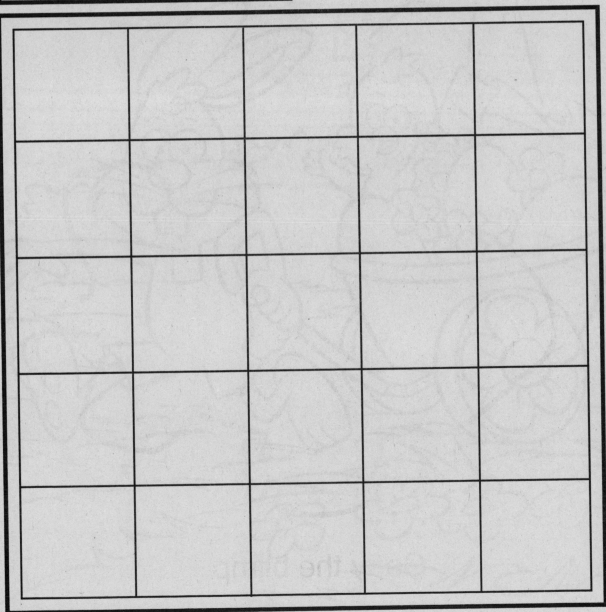

Finish the picture.

How Many Words?

Make as many words as you can out of the word or words below.

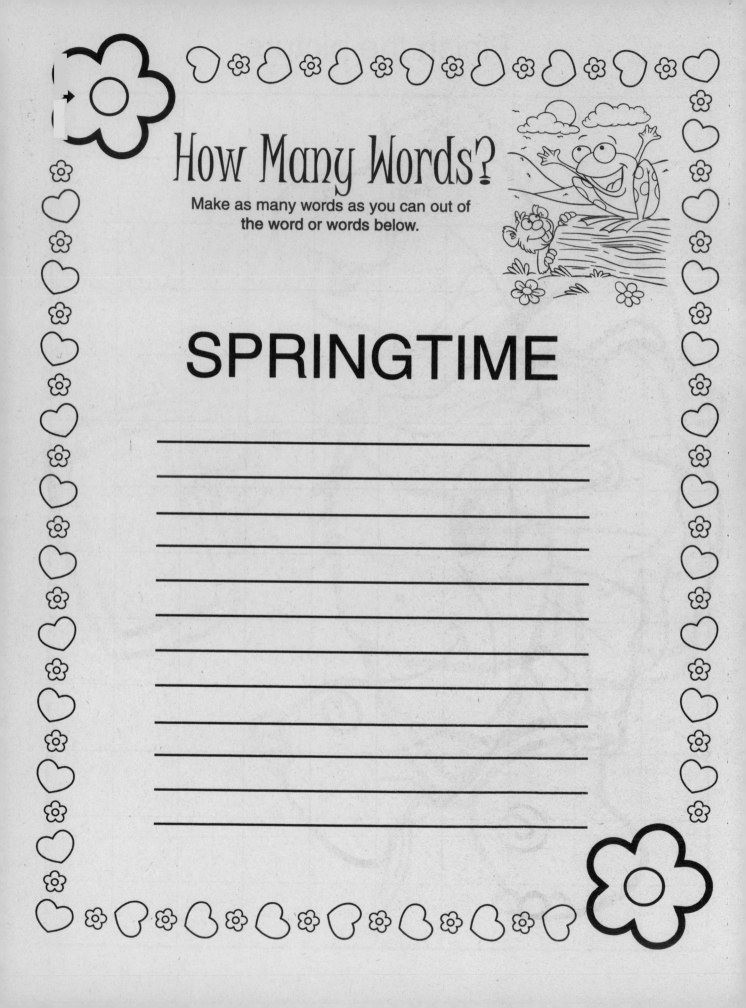

SPRINGTIME

_____

_____

_____

_____

_____

_____

_____

_____

_____

_____

Draw lines between the matching pictures.

SPRING WORD SCRAMBLE

Unscramble the spring words below.

FRLESIETTUB

_____
BUTTERFLIES

NIGWS

_____
WINGS

TBEAUILUF

_____
BEAUTIFUL

Start

Finish

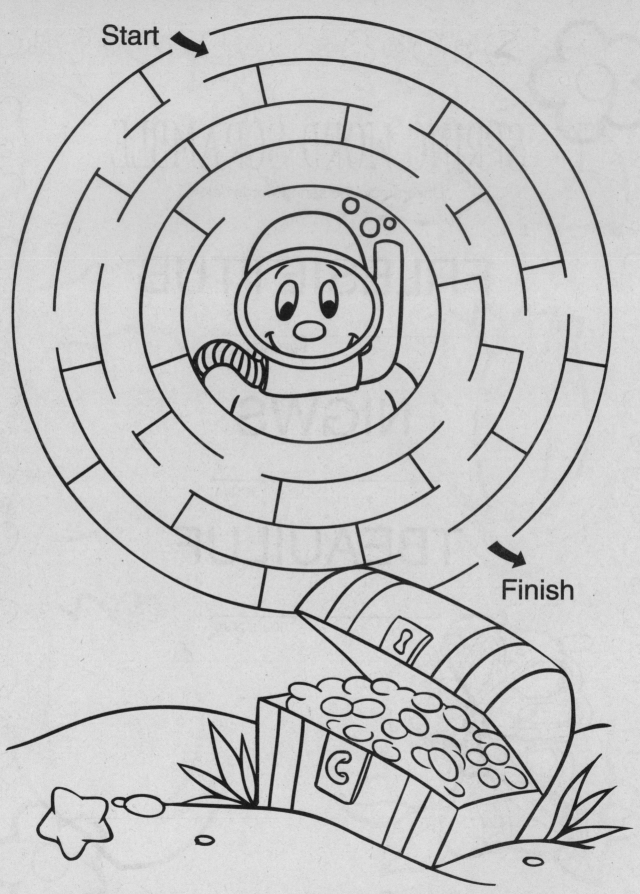

Find your way through the maze.

Draw a line from each flower to the matching outline.

Use the grid to draw the character.

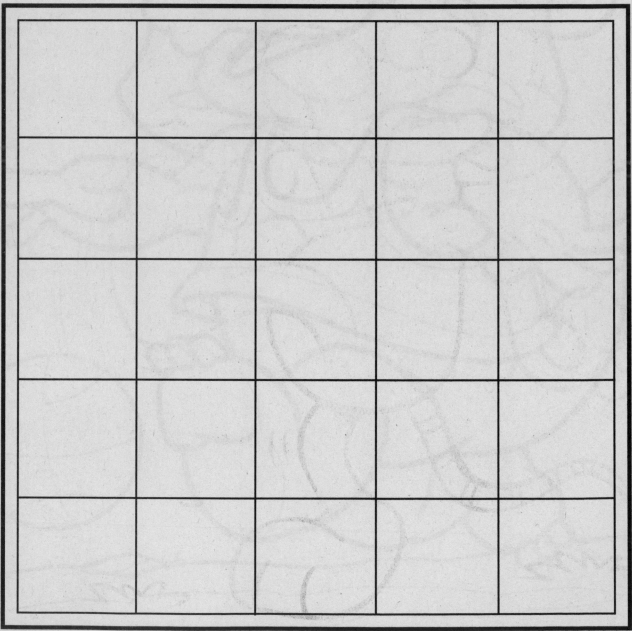

Which picture is different?

1.

2.

3.

4.